CHAMPION'S DAILY PLAYBOOK

Let's Go Win!

CHAMPION'S

DAILY

PLAYBOOK

JM Ryerson

For information or to order, please contact:
info@letsgowin.com

WWW.LETSGOWIN.COM

ISBN: 978-0-9800406-7-8
First Edition
Copyright © by Let's Go Win

Cover and interior design by Marisa Jackson

Printed in the USA

To Trey, TJ, and Lisa,
who give me everything.
And to everyone who is
committed to living their best life.

DAILY AFFIRMATION

*"Your daily affirmation is a sentence or
sentences that you repeat every day
while you journey through this guide and then beyond.
For more details on how to write an affirmation, see page 6.*

_____

_____

_____

_____

_____

_____

_____

_____

_____

_____

_____

_____

_____

_____

· PERSONAL GOALS ·

*The following seven areas are ideal for personal goal setting.
Write your goals here, and then take it a step further and type them out.
Then you can put them on your bathroom mirror where you will
see them daily. For more on how to set goals, see page 3.*

PERSONAL LIFE _____

_____

WORK LIFE _____

_____

FAMILY LIFE _____

_____

SPIRITUAL LIFE _____

_____

FINANCIAL LIFE _____

_____

MENTAL LIFE _____

_____

PHYSICAL LIFE _____

_____

"To be a
great champion
you must believe
you are the best.
If you're not,
pretend you are."
MUHAMMAD ALI

THE MUST-READ
FUNDAMENTALS OF WINNING

"I think self-awareness is probably the most important thing towards being a champion."

BILLIE JEAN KING

SUCCESS LEAVES CLUES

Sometime over the past decade, the terms *goal setting, motivation,* and *mindset* seem to have become just some other worn-out business phrases.

And believe me, I get it. With all of the supposedly foolproof ways to set goals and "rise and grind" to "take it to the next level," eventually, all of that motivational and goal setting jargon just starts to sound like noise.

I'm not here to add to the noise. In fact, my goal is to take some of it away.

That's why I want to keep things simple. We have enough complications in our lives, and that's actually part of the problem.

So, let's talk about what this playbook is and what it isn't.

First of all, I chose to call this a playbook instead of a "workbook" because I genuinely don't want this to feel like work, nor do I want it to be time-consuming. I have no interest in adding more to your already full plate.

So, consider this more like one guy's attempt to set you up to win, quite literally for the rest of your life, by tweaking a few things about your daily habits and thought processes. It really doesn't have to be hard or painful.

It just needs to be consistent.

There will be a few simple actions to carry out daily:

In the morning:
1. Set your intention for the day.
2. Repeat your affirmation.
3. Be grateful for three things.
4. Exercise your mind, body, and soul.

In the evening:
1. Check back in for a quick self-assessment.
2. Identify any triggers.
3. Rank your attitude and activity.

And that's it.

From start to finish, the daily time commitment is minimal. Still, the long-term effects of these daily actions are immeasurable.

Now, before you embark, there will be two things to do before you begin. You will fill out the first two pages of this book.

1. Choose your affirmation.

First, you will develop the life-changing affirmation that I hope will become a permanent part of your life. This will be the sentence or sentences that you repeat every day while you journey through this guide and then beyond. I'll provide some examples and give you some guidance on developing an incredible affirmation in just a moment.

2. Set your personal goals.

Goal setting may have become a cliché, but things usually become clichés for a reason. It's because goal setting is essential to discuss A LOT! We all *know* we need them. Still, because we're all so different, the way to set goals and actually ACHIEVE them is not even remotely a lock-step approach.

I know what works for me personally, but this is not meant to be a goal-setting workbook. My intention is to help you change your mindset so that you can find a way to set and reach your goals.

Change your habits, change your mindset, change your life.

From the big goals to the daily chores, writing things down is proven to be effective. Take that a step further by placing those words where you can see them daily. I put my biggest goals on my bathroom mirror to see them at least two times a day. It's been said that New Year's resolutions are 80 percent more likely to be kept when they are written down and viewed daily.

Life throws endless distractions our way. Don't force your brain to remember everything. Just write it down. If done correctly, goals give you focus, makes you accountable, encourages you to be your best, and drives you forward. The following areas are where I focus my personal goals every year. I'll also provide an example below each goal that you can use as an idea for how to set your own goal in that area.

1. **Personal Life.** What do I need to focus on this year to live my best life daily? *Example: Surround myself with people that inspire me.*

2. **Work Life.** We spend a third of our life working. Am I fulfilled doing what I'm doing? Am I giving 100 percent to the career that I have chosen? *Example: Be 100 percent present at work and then leave it there when I go home.*

3. **Family Life.** Are there any relationships with parents, kids, or siblings that need work? The quote, "The days are long, but the years are short" always comes to mind for me in this category. *Example: Be grateful and spend quality time with my family.*

4. **Spiritual Life.** How do you fill your bucket? Goals in this area could include your religion or something as simple as quiet reading time, reflection, and meditation. *Example: Meditate daily and take one nature walk per week.*

5. **Financial Life.** I encourage my family and co-workers to be wise stewards of their money, and you can do the same. Because it matters. *Example: Pay myself first (15 percent of my income), then bills, then discretionary money.*

6. **Mental Life.** Our brain is a muscle that continues to grow, so we need to feed it and exercise it. What daily habit can I start to improve myself intellectually? *Example: Read ten pages per day (or one book per month).*

7. **Physical Life.** Without our health, we really have nothing. How can we help each other make wise decisions regarding nutrition, exercise, and sleep habits? *Example: Sweat once a day.*

When you fail to set goals in just one of these areas, I've found that it makes it even harder to set and achieve goals in any of the other areas. It's like missing a piece to the incredible puzzle that is YOU! When one part is missing, you cannot see or understand the full picture. Help those around you find their missing pieces, and you will help your home and work environments become places of trust, comfort, and freedom.

These two pieces are the strong foundation—and then the morning and evening routine pieces are what you will use to build a life you love that is filled with joy and fulfillment! Now let's cover each part of the simple plan.

CHAMPION'S MORNING ROUTINE

#1 Set Your Intention

A few years ago, I started choosing one action or emotion for the day that would be my focus. Setting an intention first thing in the morning is a habit that can put you on a mindful path to make choices that align with what is most important to you.

Consider it as a conscious choice to achieve something that day or behave in a way that will lead to joy. This idea has been around for a long time in yoga and meditation circles, but you don't have to be doing yoga to make this a daily habit.

The lack of clear intention is responsible for most of the adverse or disappointing outcomes we experience. That is why *being intentional* is the solution for transforming mediocre performance, relationships, and results into exceptional ones.

With so many distractions in this world, it's easy to stay busy all day long and end up accomplishing very little. However, when you act with intention, you have a clear purpose in mind for doing what you are doing, and the result is a day filled with genuine achievement.

There are no hard and fast rules on how to set your intention. It doesn't matter if it's an attitude or an action. It could be:

- Have a growth mindset.
- Do something nice for my family.
- Plan a date night with my partner.
- Have a grateful attitude toward my spouse.
- Focus on my blessings during stressful moments.
- Finish that major project with enthusiasm.

When you act with intention, you give all of your focus and energy to a singular task or person. You'll find that once you give everything you have to one thing, you'll get better results and end up spending less time overall on daily tasks.

It can be general or specific. The important thing is to verbalize it so that you're very clear.

Set it, say it, execute on it.

#2 Say Your Daily Affirmation

We talk to ourselves every single day. If you are thinking to yourself, "I don't talk to myself," then all you did was prove my point.

What are you saying, though? Is it good, bad, or indifferent?

All too often our internal dialogue is not serving your best interests and, in reality, actually incredibly damaging.

This is where your daily affirmation comes in to save the day. Adding a positive daily affirmation to your life can create a massive wave of momentum and help ensure you are changing the narrative. I coach all my clients to develop and employ daily affirmations for the following reasons:

Improve Health. Studies have proven that people who think positively tend to feel better and live longer than those who don't. You get to choose what you want to believe and how you feel. One of my favorite quotes by Lao Tzu is, "Watch your thoughts; they become words. Watch your words; they become actions. Watch your actions; they become habits. Watch your habits; they become character. Watch your character; it becomes your destiny." It all starts with your thoughts, so choose the right ideas and words that will set you up for success.

Increase Confidence. Hardwiring begins before you ever even have a long-term memory. Some of those hardwires are positive, and others are negative. Positive affirmations help you disregard the self-limiting beliefs that others have put upon you. Tell yourself that you are confident, strong, and capable, and you are much more likely to embody those beliefs. Hardwires were put in place over many years, so it won't happen overnight. Still, the daily practice will eventually work to reprogram yourself.

Be Inspiring. The definition of an affirmation is the assertion that something exists or is true. Positive affirmations help us focus on the good in our lives instead of the negative. Failure no longer exists, but rather is a chance to learn and try new things. We all want to be inspired in life, so why not do it for yourself? Create your affirmation today and inspire yourself and those around you by showing up as the best version of you.

This doesn't have to be hard or complicated, and your affirmation can be long or short. Here are a few examples of simple daily affirmations:

- I am strong, confident, and capable.
- My body is healthy, my mind is brilliant, and my soul is tranquil.
- Positivity is a choice, and I choose to be positive.
- I am happy, generous, and successful.

There are so many potentially detrimental habits and attitudes that we are hardwired with during childhood. Your daily affirmation is one great way to help reset your wiring so that you default to thoughts like, "I'm a winner, and I am confident."

It's been said that 80 percent of our hardwiring about the world and ourselves is in place by the time we're five years old. So, if your parents had a dysfunctional relationship with money, then guess what? There's a high likelihood that you inherited that.

A brain is a programmable machine—and that means it's going to need some tweaking now and again. Yet, after childhood, we've been told that our programming is set and there's no changing it.

Let me tell you that this is simply not true.

We can overcome anything. The key is *consciousness* and *awareness* of the underlying issue or attitude.

Most of us operate without ever thinking, "Why do I believe this?" Suppose you were to go to a college campus and ask college students why they believe a certain way. Many of them will respond with, "Because my parents do" or possibly, "I just do."

That is an example of hardwiring.

I grew up in a home with a lot of love! My parents were great, but they weren't perfect (just like you and me). Often, childhood positivity and innocence can be overshadowed by prejudices and other ingrained ways of thinking.

As an example, whenever my dad met someone who was a member of a country club or drove a nice car, he called them "pretty people." The pretty people had a lot of money, and in my mind, this was a negative or derogatory nickname.

So, when I started to make good money as an adult, I struggled with shame and guilt about it. It's not that I thought money was evil— just that it wasn't meant for me. It took years for me to reverse this hardwiring.

Knowing the importance of wiring has changed the way I talk to my kids. I used to say things like, "Look how gifted/smart you are." The problem with this type of accolade is what happens when your kid gets a bad grade? Is it because he's not smart enough?

No. In that case, it's probably because he didn't study enough or possibly simply didn't understand the concept and needs it explained in a different way. That doesn't make him "less smart," but our brains are tricky that way.

So, choose affirmations carefully, and make sure that they instill the right attitudes and emotions, such as:

Treating others with kindness.

Being courageous and bold.

Having a strong work ethic.

Being vulnerable and ready to love and be loved.

These are all the things we should be working toward!

It may take a long time before you actually believe what you are saying, but just do yourself a favor and stick with it. Say it for long enough, and eventually you can get rid of your faulty wiring and replace it with wiring that leads to the brightest possible future!

#3 Be Grateful

This one really doesn't need much explanation. Every day, you have literally hundreds of things to be grateful for. Being alive, having food on your table, having a roof over your head, family, a car, a dog, a job, working legs, fingers, toes, a bed…. the list could go on and on!

Gratitude involves recognition of the positive things in your life and how they affect you. This can range from acknowledging a beautiful flower you pass on the sidewalk to the feeling of relief that comes from recovering from a severe illness.

From daily journaling to evening prayers, gratitude practice can take many forms. For the purposes of this playbook, we're keeping it simple. I just want you to name three things, and it can even be one-word responses (as in "kids" or "lungs" or "house").

What better way to start each day than naming things that make your life better? It puts out positive energy and encourages momentum.

#4 Exercise Mind, Body, and Soul

We live in a hectic world and have many responsibilities daily. I watch most of my friends taking care of everyone and everything around them, but never really caring for themselves. At some point, you *will* reach a breaking point if this pattern continues.

I am about to tell you something that may sound selfish at the outset, but it's actually the polar opposite.

To take care of everyone else, you must take care of yourself first.

On an airplane, the flight attendant always tells adults to put on their oxygen mask first so they will be able to help their kids. It's the same idea here. When people neglect themselves, they are unable physically or mentally to help others long term.

The great news is that there are only three areas that need to be addressed to be your best:

1. **Mind.** Much research has been done on the fact that our brains continue to develop as we age. This is a concept known as *neuroplasticity*. You are welcome to look deeper into this idea but let me say that exercising your mind is an essential piece of the puzzle. Some suggestions are playing brain games (my favorite is Lumosity), learning something new, and reading at least ten pages from a book a day. Our brains are meant to be exercised regularly and, like any muscle, will atrophy if not challenged daily. Learning does not stop once school is over, so challenge your mind daily.

2. **Body.** "The greatest wealth is health." That simple quote by Virgil has profound meaning and something that we should all keep as perspective. We only have one body, and it is meant to move and be well-nourished. There are so many different forms of exercise, such as taking a walk, lifting weights, and practicing yoga. I teach my clients the "sweat once daily" mantra for taking

care of their bodies. Our health is precious, so checking off that box helps ensure our bodies stay healthy for as long as possible.

3. **Soul.** According to Merriam-Webster, the definition of soul is "the spiritual principle embodied in human beings, all rational and spiritual beings, or the universe." The soul is that part of you that is hard to define, but you know it's there. One could argue that the soul is our entire being. Feeding your soul can be accomplished in many ways, such as meditating (my personal favorite), reading the Bible, praying, or walking in silence along the beach. Whatever you choose, take time for yourself to be grounded and centered.

The three areas require daily *intentional* effort. Those who depend on you need you to show up as the best version of yourself. Kakul Sinha said it best: "Self-care is breath for the soul. Without taking care of yourself, your mind, body, and soul deplete. How can you love another when you are last on your list?"

CHAMPION'S EVENING ROUTINE

#1 Assess How You Feel

After a long and productive day of acting upon your set intention, practicing gratitude, and living according to your affirmation, you should feel a little differently. Hopefully the changes are good, but they may not always be.

Living consciously means being aware of all changes and acknowledging them.

The "how am I feeling" section is your opportunity to reflect upon the day. No one will ever see this page but you, so let it out and be honest! Vent if you need to! Better yet, remember all the good things that happened.

You may not get a do-over on the day. However, suppose you acknowledge a negative attitude or action. In that case, it could help ensure that you don't have the same issue again.

#2 Identify Positive Triggers

I'd love to tell you that I am at my best every single day, but that would be a lie. We all have great days, and we all have days that just don't pan out thanks to unforeseen "triggers" that do their best to derail us and steal our joy.

I have coached on this subject for years as I believe it's one of the most critical ingredients in being our very best. The best definition for *trigger* I could find is this:

> **Trigger:** *to cause (an event or situation) to happen or exist.*

If you research it more deeply, the word *trigger* is almost always associated with negativity, but there are also positive triggers! While negative triggers certainly exist, let's focus on positive triggers and how to combat the negative ones.

A trigger can be different for every person, and there is undoubtedly no one type. For some, a good trigger could be reading a quote, meditating, or clapping their hands. For me, it has always been listening to music. When I made daily sales calls early on in my career, there was a song by Eminem that made me feel like I could leap from rooftop to rooftop. I can't explain why that particular song lit a fire inside, but it did.

Certain songs put me in the proper mindset, and like a light switch being turned on, instantly I am the best and brightest version of myself.

How do you discover your triggers? The simplest way is through self-reflection and paying attention to what "revs your engine." Then, when you find it, write it down. It will undoubtedly become a habit once you use the trigger several hundred times. Still, it's always nice to have a reference point in case of temporary amnesia.

Now that you have your trigger at your disposal, it's time to use it to your advantage. Life happens, and that means some form of adversity or challenge is always right around the corner. As I stated earlier, we also have negative triggers that don't allow us to be our best. When these negative triggers pop up, hit back with your positive trigger and see which one prevails.

This technique may not always work, but a trigger is simply one more tool you can use to show up as your best version. You and the world deserve your very best. Your trigger can help unlock that version more often!

#3 Rank Your Attitude and Activity

Your last task for the evening is a simple attitude and activity ranking. I added this because I like to see how my attitude and activity levels corresponded to my motivating triggers and what I chose as my intention for the day.

The two things you are in complete control of are your attitude and your activity. Take control of those two aspects and they will transform your outcomes.

Use these two scales in any way you choose. This is your playbook and your life.

Make the best of both!

THE BIG PICTURE

My ultimate vision is to inspire people to live their best lives.

Doing these daily exercises puts people in the best position to win every single day. This is so important because self-limiting beliefs are quite literally my *least* favorite thing in the world. We are all capable of so much more!

In my book, *Let's Go Win*, I discuss in greater detail how to reprogram your mind to switch into CHAMPION mode, every single day. I encourage you to pick up a copy if you are interested in digging even more deeply into the subject.

There is so much negativity in the world. It's really an endless onslaught. The goal of this playbook is to help you learn how to focus on the positive. I want you to focus on what you CAN do and what you CAN accomplish instead of what you CANNOT.

Positivity breeds more positive activity, which breeds more positivity. It's like the best domino effect ever.

I hope this playbook is simple enough for you to engage with every day without it feeling like a burden. If something is simple enough, it can more easily become a part of your routine.

Don't let self-care be an isolated event. Make it a way of life! When you are at your best, you can help those you love to live their best lives as well.

So, let's all go win!

Set your intention for the day:

Energy – eat healthy No sugar.

☐

Repeat my daily affirmation

· DAILY GRATITUDE ·

I am grateful for:

1. ....

2. ....

3. ....

☐ ## EXERCISE MY MIND
Play brain games, learn something new, read ten pages from a book

☐ ## EXERCISE MY BODY
Go for a walk, lift weights, do yoga, ride a bike

☐ ## EXERCISE MY SOUL
Meditate, read the Bible, listen to spiritual music

How am I feeling today?

_____
_____
_____
_____

What triggers did I experience today?

_____
_____
_____

HOW WAS MY ATTITUDE TODAY?

Score 1 to 5, 1 being the lowest, 5 being the highest.

| 1 | 2 | 3 | 4 | 5 |

HOW WAS MY ACTIVITY TODAY?

Score 1 to 5, 1 being the lowest, 5 being the highest.

| 1 | 2 | 3 | 4 | 5 |

Notes: _____
_____
_____

Set your intention for the day:

_____

_____

☐

Repeat my daily affirmation

· DAILY GRATITUDE ·

I am grateful for:

1. _____

2. _____

3. _____

☐ **EXERCISE MY MIND**
Play brain games, learn something new, read ten pages from a book

☐ **EXERCISE MY BODY**
Go for a walk, lift weights, do yoga, ride a bike

☐ **EXERCISE MY SOUL**
Meditate, read the Bible, listen to spiritual music

How am I feeling today?

_____

_____

_____

_____

What triggers did I experience today?

_____

_____

_____

HOW WAS MY ATTITUDE TODAY?

Score 1 to 5, 1 being the lowest, 5 being the highest.

| 1 | 2 | 3 | 4 | 5 |

HOW WAS MY ACTIVITY TODAY?

Score 1 to 5, 1 being the lowest, 5 being the highest.

| 1 | 2 | 3 | 4 | 5 |

Notes: _____

_____

_____

Set your intention for the day:

_____

_____

☐

Repeat my daily affirmation

· DAILY GRATITUDE ·

I am grateful for:

1. _____

2. _____

3. _____

☐ **EXERCISE MY MIND**
Play brain games, learn something new, read ten pages from a book

☐ **EXERCISE MY BODY**
Go for a walk, lift weights, do yoga, ride a bike

☐ **EXERCISE MY SOUL**
Meditate, read the Bible, listen to spiritual music

How am I feeling today?

_____

_____

_____

_____

What triggers did I experience today?

_____

_____

_____

HOW WAS MY ATTITUDE TODAY?

Score 1 to 5, 1 being the lowest, 5 being the highest.

| 1 | 2 | 3 | 4 | 5 |

HOW WAS MY ACTIVITY TODAY?

Score 1 to 5, 1 being the lowest, 5 being the highest.

| 1 | 2 | 3 | 4 | 5 |

Notes: _____

_____

_____

Date:

Set your intention for the day:

_____

_____

☐

Repeat my daily affirmation

· DAILY GRATITUDE ·

I am grateful for:

1. _____

2. _____

3. _____

☐ **EXERCISE MY MIND**
Play brain games, learn something new, read ten pages from a book

☐ **EXERCISE MY BODY**
Go for a walk, lift weights, do yoga, ride a bike

☐ **EXERCISE MY SOUL**
Meditate, read the Bible, listen to spiritual music

How am I feeling today?

_____
_____
_____
_____

What triggers did I experience today?

_____
_____
_____

HOW WAS MY ATTITUDE TODAY?

Score 1 to 5, 1 being the lowest, 5 being the highest.

| 1 | 2 | 3 | 4 | 5 |

HOW WAS MY ACTIVITY TODAY?

Score 1 to 5, 1 being the lowest, 5 being the highest.

| 1 | 2 | 3 | 4 | 5 |

Notes: _____
_____
_____

Date:

Set your intention for the day:

☐

Repeat my daily affirmation

· DAILY GRATITUDE ·

I am grateful for:

1.
2.
3.

☐ **EXERCISE MY MIND**
Play brain games, learn something new, read ten pages from a book

☐ **EXERCISE MY BODY**
Go for a walk, lift weights, do yoga, ride a bike

☐ **EXERCISE MY SOUL**
Meditate, read the Bible, listen to spiritual music

How am I feeling today?

_____

_____

_____

_____

What triggers did I experience today?

_____

_____

_____

HOW WAS MY ATTITUDE TODAY?

Score 1 to 5, 1 being the lowest, 5 being the highest.

| 1 | 2 | 3 | 4 | 5 |

HOW WAS MY ACTIVITY TODAY?

Score 1 to 5, 1 being the lowest, 5 being the highest.

| 1 | 2 | 3 | 4 | 5 |

Notes: _____

_____

_____

Set your intention for the day:

_____

_____

☐

Repeat my daily affirmation

· DAILY GRATITUDE ·

I am grateful for:

1. _____

2. _____

3. _____

☐ **EXERCISE MY MIND**
Play brain games, learn something new, read ten pages from a book

☐ **EXERCISE MY BODY**
Go for a walk, lift weights, do yoga, ride a bike

☐ **EXERCISE MY SOUL**
Meditate, read the Bible, listen to spiritual music

How am I feeling today?

_____

_____

_____

_____

What triggers did I experience today?

_____

_____

_____

HOW WAS MY ATTITUDE TODAY?

Score 1 to 5, 1 being the lowest, 5 being the highest.

| 1 | 2 | 3 | 4 | 5 |

HOW WAS MY ACTIVITY TODAY?

Score 1 to 5, 1 being the lowest, 5 being the highest.

| 1 | 2 | 3 | 4 | 5 |

Notes: _____

_____

_____

Date:

Set your intention for the day:

_____

_____

☐

Repeat my daily affirmation

· DAILY GRATITUDE ·

I am grateful for:

1. _____

2. _____

3. _____

☐ **EXERCISE MY MIND**
Play brain games, learn something new, read ten pages from a book

☐ **EXERCISE MY BODY**
Go for a walk, lift weights, do yoga, ride a bike

☐ **EXERCISE MY SOUL**
Meditate, read the Bible, listen to spiritual music

How am I feeling today?

_____

_____

_____

_____

What triggers did I experience today?

_____

_____

_____

HOW WAS MY ATTITUDE TODAY?

Score 1 to 5, 1 being the lowest, 5 being the highest.

| 1 | 2 | 3 | 4 | 5 |

HOW WAS MY ACTIVITY TODAY?

Score 1 to 5, 1 being the lowest, 5 being the highest.

| 1 | 2 | 3 | 4 | 5 |

Notes: _____

_____

_____

Set your intention for the day:

_____

_____

☐

Repeat my daily affirmation

· DAILY GRATITUDE ·

I am grateful for:

1. _____

2. _____

3. _____

☐ **EXERCISE MY MIND**
Play brain games, learn something new, read ten pages from a book

☐ **EXERCISE MY BODY**
Go for a walk, lift weights, do yoga, ride a bike

☐ **EXERCISE MY SOUL**
Meditate, read the Bible, listen to spiritual music

How am I feeling today?

_____

_____

_____

_____

What triggers did I experience today?

_____

_____

_____

HOW WAS MY ATTITUDE TODAY?

Score 1 to 5, 1 being the lowest, 5 being the highest.

| 1 | 2 | 3 | 4 | 5 |

HOW WAS MY ACTIVITY TODAY?

Score 1 to 5, 1 being the lowest, 5 being the highest.

| 1 | 2 | 3 | 4 | 5 |

Notes: _____

_____

_____

Date:

Set your intention for the day:

_____

_____

☐

Repeat my daily affirmation

· DAILY GRATITUDE ·

I am grateful for:

1. ....

2. ....

3. ....

☐ **EXERCISE MY MIND**
Play brain games, learn something new, read ten pages from a book

☐ **EXERCISE MY BODY**
Go for a walk, lift weights, do yoga, ride a bike

☐ **EXERCISE MY SOUL**
Meditate, read the Bible, listen to spiritual music

How am I feeling today?

_____

_____

_____

_____

What triggers did I experience today?

_____

_____

_____

HOW WAS MY ATTITUDE TODAY?

Score 1 to 5, 1 being the lowest, 5 being the highest.

| 1 | 2 | 3 | 4 | 5 |

HOW WAS MY ACTIVITY TODAY?

Score 1 to 5, 1 being the lowest, 5 being the highest.

| 1 | 2 | 3 | 4 | 5 |

Notes: _____

_____

_____

Set your intention for the day:

_____

_____

☐

Repeat my daily affirmation

· DAILY GRATITUDE ·

I am grateful for:

1. ....

2. ....

3. ....

☐ **EXERCISE MY MIND**
Play brain games, learn something new, read ten pages from a book

☐ **EXERCISE MY BODY**
Go for a walk, lift weights, do yoga, ride a bike

☐ **EXERCISE MY SOUL**
Meditate, read the Bible, listen to spiritual music

How am I feeling today?

_____

_____

_____

_____

What triggers did I experience today?

_____

_____

_____

HOW WAS MY ATTITUDE TODAY?

Score 1 to 5, 1 being the lowest, 5 being the highest.

| 1 | 2 | 3 | 4 | 5 |

HOW WAS MY ACTIVITY TODAY?

Score 1 to 5, 1 being the lowest, 5 being the highest.

| 1 | 2 | 3 | 4 | 5 |

Notes: _____

_____

_____

Set your intention for the day:

_____

_____

☐

Repeat my daily affirmation

· DAILY GRATITUDE ·

I am grateful for:

1. _____

2. _____

3. _____

☐ **EXERCISE MY MIND**
Play brain games, learn something new, read ten pages from a book

☐ **EXERCISE MY BODY**
Go for a walk, lift weights, do yoga, ride a bike

☐ **EXERCISE MY SOUL**
Meditate, read the Bible, listen to spiritual music

How am I feeling today?

_____

_____

_____

_____

What triggers did I experience today?

_____

_____

_____

HOW WAS MY ATTITUDE TODAY?

Score 1 to 5, 1 being the lowest, 5 being the highest.

| 1 | 2 | 3 | 4 | 5 |

HOW WAS MY ACTIVITY TODAY?

Score 1 to 5, 1 being the lowest, 5 being the highest.

| 1 | 2 | 3 | 4 | 5 |

Notes: _____

_____

_____

Set your intention for the day:

☐

Repeat my daily affirmation

· DAILY GRATITUDE ·

I am grateful for:

1.
2.
3.

☐ ## EXERCISE MY MIND
Play brain games, learn something new, read ten pages from a book

☐ ## EXERCISE MY BODY
Go for a walk, lift weights, do yoga, ride a bike

☐ ## EXERCISE MY SOUL
Meditate, read the Bible, listen to spiritual music

How am I feeling today?

_____

_____

_____

_____

What triggers did I experience today?

_____

_____

_____

HOW WAS MY ATTITUDE TODAY?

Score 1 to 5, 1 being the lowest, 5 being the highest.

| 1 | 2 | 3 | 4 | 5 |

HOW WAS MY ACTIVITY TODAY?

Score 1 to 5, 1 being the lowest, 5 being the highest.

| 1 | 2 | 3 | 4 | 5 |

Notes: _____

_____

_____

Set your intention for the day:

_____

_____

☐

Repeat my daily affirmation

· DAILY GRATITUDE ·

I am grateful for:

1. _____

2. _____

3. _____

☐ **EXERCISE MY MIND**
Play brain games, learn something new, read ten pages from a book

☐ **EXERCISE MY BODY**
Go for a walk, lift weights, do yoga, ride a bike

☐ **EXERCISE MY SOUL**
Meditate, read the Bible, listen to spiritual music

How am I feeling today?

_____

_____

_____

_____

What triggers did I experience today?

_____

_____

_____

HOW WAS MY ATTITUDE TODAY?

Score 1 to 5, 1 being the lowest, 5 being the highest.

| 1 | 2 | 3 | 4 | 5 |

HOW WAS MY ACTIVITY TODAY?

Score 1 to 5, 1 being the lowest, 5 being the highest.

| 1 | 2 | 3 | 4 | 5 |

Notes: _____

_____

_____

Set your intention for the day:

_____

_____

☐

Repeat my daily affirmation

· DAILY GRATITUDE ·

I am grateful for:

1. _____

2. _____

3. _____

☐ **EXERCISE MY MIND**
Play brain games, learn something new, read ten pages from a book

☐ **EXERCISE MY BODY**
Go for a walk, lift weights, do yoga, ride a bike

☐ **EXERCISE MY SOUL**
Meditate, read the Bible, listen to spiritual music

How am I feeling today?

_____

_____

_____

_____

What triggers did I experience today?

_____

_____

_____

HOW WAS MY ATTITUDE TODAY?

Score 1 to 5, 1 being the lowest, 5 being the highest.

| 1 | 2 | 3 | 4 | 5 |

HOW WAS MY ACTIVITY TODAY?

Score 1 to 5, 1 being the lowest, 5 being the highest.

| 1 | 2 | 3 | 4 | 5 |

Notes: _____

_____

_____

Set your intention for the day:

☐

Repeat my daily affirmation

· DAILY GRATITUDE ·

I am grateful for:

1. _____

2. _____

3. _____

☐ **EXERCISE MY MIND**
Play brain games, learn something new, read ten pages from a book

☐ **EXERCISE MY BODY**
Go for a walk, lift weights, do yoga, ride a bike

☐ **EXERCISE MY SOUL**
Meditate, read the Bible, listen to spiritual music

How am I feeling today?

_____

_____

_____

_____

What triggers did I experience today?

_____

_____

_____

HOW WAS MY ATTITUDE TODAY?

Score 1 to 5, 1 being the lowest, 5 being the highest.

| 1 | 2 | 3 | 4 | 5 |

HOW WAS MY ACTIVITY TODAY?

Score 1 to 5, 1 being the lowest, 5 being the highest.

| 1 | 2 | 3 | 4 | 5 |

Notes: _____

_____

_____

Set your intention for the day:

_____

_____

☐

Repeat my daily affirmation

· DAILY GRATITUDE ·

I am grateful for:

1. _____

2. _____

3. _____

☐ **EXERCISE MY MIND**
Play brain games, learn something new, read ten pages from a book

☐ **EXERCISE MY BODY**
Go for a walk, lift weights, do yoga, ride a bike

☐ **EXERCISE MY SOUL**
Meditate, read the Bible, listen to spiritual music

How am I feeling today?

_____

_____

_____

_____

What triggers did I experience today?

_____

_____

_____

HOW WAS MY ATTITUDE TODAY?

Score 1 to 5, 1 being the lowest, 5 being the highest.

| 1 | 2 | 3 | 4 | 5 |

HOW WAS MY ACTIVITY TODAY?

Score 1 to 5, 1 being the lowest, 5 being the highest.

| 1 | 2 | 3 | 4 | 5 |

Notes: _____

_____

_____

Set your intention for the day:

_____

_____

☐

Repeat my daily affirmation

· DAILY GRATITUDE ·

I am grateful for:

1. _____

2. _____

3. _____

☐ **EXERCISE MY MIND**
Play brain games, learn something new, read ten pages from a book

☐ **EXERCISE MY BODY**
Go for a walk, lift weights, do yoga, ride a bike

☐ **EXERCISE MY SOUL**
Meditate, read the Bible, listen to spiritual music

How am I feeling today?

_____

_____

_____

_____

What triggers did I experience today?

_____

_____

_____

HOW WAS MY ATTITUDE TODAY?

Score 1 to 5, 1 being the lowest, 5 being the highest.

| 1 | 2 | 3 | 4 | 5 |

HOW WAS MY ACTIVITY TODAY?

Score 1 to 5, 1 being the lowest, 5 being the highest.

| 1 | 2 | 3 | 4 | 5 |

Notes: _____

_____

_____

Set your intention for the day:

_____

_____

☐

Repeat my daily affirmation

· DAILY GRATITUDE ·

I am grateful for:

1. _____

2. _____

3. _____

☐ **EXERCISE MY MIND**
Play brain games, learn something new, read ten pages from a book

☐ **EXERCISE MY BODY**
Go for a walk, lift weights, do yoga, ride a bike

☐ **EXERCISE MY SOUL**
Meditate, read the Bible, listen to spiritual music

How am I feeling today?

_____

_____

_____

_____

What triggers did I experience today?

_____

_____

_____

HOW WAS MY ATTITUDE TODAY?

Score 1 to 5, 1 being the lowest, 5 being the highest.

| 1 | 2 | 3 | 4 | 5 |

HOW WAS MY ACTIVITY TODAY?

Score 1 to 5, 1 being the lowest, 5 being the highest.

| 1 | 2 | 3 | 4 | 5 |

Notes: _____

_____

_____

Set your intention for the day:

_____

_____

☐

Repeat my daily affirmation

· DAILY GRATITUDE ·

I am grateful for:

1. _____

2. _____

3. _____

☐ **EXERCISE MY MIND**
Play brain games, learn something new, read ten pages from a book

☐ **EXERCISE MY BODY**
Go for a walk, lift weights, do yoga, ride a bike

☐ **EXERCISE MY SOUL**
Meditate, read the Bible, listen to spiritual music

How am I feeling today?

_____

_____

_____

_____

What triggers did I experience today?

_____

_____

_____

HOW WAS MY ATTITUDE TODAY?

Score 1 to 5, 1 being the lowest, 5 being the highest.

| 1 | 2 | 3 | 4 | 5 |

HOW WAS MY ACTIVITY TODAY?

Score 1 to 5, 1 being the lowest, 5 being the highest.

| 1 | 2 | 3 | 4 | 5 |

Notes: _____

_____

_____

Set your intention for the day:

_____

_____

☐

Repeat my daily affirmation

· DAILY GRATITUDE ·

I am grateful for:

1. _____

2. _____

3. _____

☐ **EXERCISE MY MIND**
Play brain games, learn something new, read ten pages from a book

☐ **EXERCISE MY BODY**
Go for a walk, lift weights, do yoga, ride a bike

☐ **EXERCISE MY SOUL**
Meditate, read the Bible, listen to spiritual music

How am I feeling today?

_____

_____

_____

_____

What triggers did I experience today?

_____

_____

_____

HOW WAS MY ATTITUDE TODAY?

Score 1 to 5, 1 being the lowest, 5 being the highest.

| 1 | 2 | 3 | 4 | 5 |

HOW WAS MY ACTIVITY TODAY?

Score 1 to 5, 1 being the lowest, 5 being the highest.

| 1 | 2 | 3 | 4 | 5 |

Notes: _____

_____

_____

Set your intention for the day:

☐

Repeat my daily affirmation

· DAILY GRATITUDE ·

I am grateful for:

1.

2.

3.

☐ **EXERCISE MY MIND**
Play brain games, learn something new, read ten pages from a book

☐ **EXERCISE MY BODY**
Go for a walk, lift weights, do yoga, ride a bike

☐ **EXERCISE MY SOUL**
Meditate, read the Bible, listen to spiritual music

How am I feeling today?

_____

_____

_____

_____

What triggers did I experience today?

_____

_____

_____

HOW WAS MY ATTITUDE TODAY?

Score 1 to 5, 1 being the lowest, 5 being the highest.

| 1 | 2 | 3 | 4 | 5 |

HOW WAS MY ACTIVITY TODAY?

Score 1 to 5, 1 being the lowest, 5 being the highest.

| 1 | 2 | 3 | 4 | 5 |

Notes: _____

_____

_____

Set your intention for the day:

_____

_____

☐

Repeat my daily affirmation

· DAILY GRATITUDE ·

I am grateful for:

1. _____

2. _____

3. _____

☐ **EXERCISE MY MIND**
   Play brain games, learn something new, read ten pages from a book

☐ **EXERCISE MY BODY**
   Go for a walk, lift weights, do yoga, ride a bike

☐ **EXERCISE MY SOUL**
   Meditate, read the Bible, listen to spiritual music

How am I feeling today?

_____

_____

_____

_____

What triggers did I experience today?

_____

_____

_____

HOW WAS MY ATTITUDE TODAY?

Score 1 to 5, 1 being the lowest, 5 being the highest.

| 1 | 2 | 3 | 4 | 5 |

HOW WAS MY ACTIVITY TODAY?

Score 1 to 5, 1 being the lowest, 5 being the highest.

| 1 | 2 | 3 | 4 | 5 |

Notes: _____

_____

_____

Set your intention for the day:

_____

_____

☐

Repeat my daily affirmation

· DAILY GRATITUDE ·

I am grateful for:

1. _____

2. _____

3. _____

☐ **EXERCISE MY MIND**
Play brain games, learn something new, read ten pages from a book

☐ **EXERCISE MY BODY**
Go for a walk, lift weights, do yoga, ride a bike

☐ **EXERCISE MY SOUL**
Meditate, read the Bible, listen to spiritual music

How am I feeling today?

_____

_____

_____

_____

What triggers did I experience today?

_____

_____

_____

HOW WAS MY ATTITUDE TODAY?

Score 1 to 5, 1 being the lowest, 5 being the highest.

| 1 | 2 | 3 | 4 | 5 |

HOW WAS MY ACTIVITY TODAY?

Score 1 to 5, 1 being the lowest, 5 being the highest.

| 1 | 2 | 3 | 4 | 5 |

Notes: _____

_____

_____

Set your intention for the day:

_____

_____

☐

Repeat my daily affirmation

· DAILY GRATITUDE ·

I am grateful for:

1. _____

2. _____

3. _____

☐ **EXERCISE MY MIND**
Play brain games, learn something new, read ten pages from a book

☐ **EXERCISE MY BODY**
Go for a walk, lift weights, do yoga, ride a bike

☐ **EXERCISE MY SOUL**
Meditate, read the Bible, listen to spiritual music

How am I feeling today?

_____

_____

_____

_____

What triggers did I experience today?

_____

_____

_____

HOW WAS MY ATTITUDE TODAY?

Score 1 to 5, 1 being the lowest, 5 being the highest.

| 1 | 2 | 3 | 4 | 5 |

HOW WAS MY ACTIVITY TODAY?

Score 1 to 5, 1 being the lowest, 5 being the highest.

| 1 | 2 | 3 | 4 | 5 |

Notes: _____

_____

_____

Set your intention for the day:

_____

_____

☐

Repeat my daily affirmation

· DAILY GRATITUDE ·

I am grateful for:

1. _____

2. _____

3. _____

☐ **EXERCISE MY MIND**
Play brain games, learn something new, read ten pages from a book

☐ **EXERCISE MY BODY**
Go for a walk, lift weights, do yoga, ride a bike

☐ **EXERCISE MY SOUL**
Meditate, read the Bible, listen to spiritual music

How am I feeling today?

_____

_____

_____

_____

What triggers did I experience today?

_____

_____

_____

_____

HOW WAS MY ATTITUDE TODAY?

Score 1 to 5, 1 being the lowest, 5 being the highest.

| 1 | 2 | 3 | 4 | 5 |

HOW WAS MY ACTIVITY TODAY?

Score 1 to 5, 1 being the lowest, 5 being the highest.

| 1 | 2 | 3 | 4 | 5 |

Notes: _____

_____

_____

Date:

Set your intention for the day:

_____

_____

□

Repeat my daily affirmation

· DAILY GRATITUDE ·

I am grateful for:

1. _____

2. _____

3. _____

□ **EXERCISE MY MIND**
Play brain games, learn something new, read ten pages from a book

□ **EXERCISE MY BODY**
Go for a walk, lift weights, do yoga, ride a bike

□ **EXERCISE MY SOUL**
Meditate, read the Bible, listen to spiritual music

How am I feeling today?

_____

_____

_____

_____

What triggers did I experience today?

_____

_____

_____

HOW WAS MY ATTITUDE TODAY?

Score 1 to 5, 1 being the lowest, 5 being the highest.

| 1 | 2 | 3 | 4 | 5 |

HOW WAS MY ACTIVITY TODAY?

Score 1 to 5, 1 being the lowest, 5 being the highest.

| 1 | 2 | 3 | 4 | 5 |

Notes: _____

_____

_____

Set your intention for the day:

_____

_____

☐

Repeat my daily affirmation

· DAILY GRATITUDE ·

I am grateful for:

1. _____

2. _____

3. _____

☐ **EXERCISE MY MIND**
Play brain games, learn something new, read ten pages from a book

☐ **EXERCISE MY BODY**
Go for a walk, lift weights, do yoga, ride a bike

☐ **EXERCISE MY SOUL**
Meditate, read the Bible, listen to spiritual music

How am I feeling today?

_____

_____

_____

_____

What triggers did I experience today?

_____

_____

_____

HOW WAS MY ATTITUDE TODAY?

Score 1 to 5, 1 being the lowest, 5 being the highest.

| 1 | 2 | 3 | 4 | 5 |

HOW WAS MY ACTIVITY TODAY?

Score 1 to 5, 1 being the lowest, 5 being the highest.

| 1 | 2 | 3 | 4 | 5 |

Notes: _____

_____

_____

Set your intention for the day:

_____

_____

☐

Repeat my daily affirmation

· DAILY GRATITUDE ·

I am grateful for:

1. _____

2. _____

3. _____

☐ ## EXERCISE MY MIND
Play brain games, learn something new, read ten pages from a book

☐ ## EXERCISE MY BODY
Go for a walk, lift weights, do yoga, ride a bike

☐ ## EXERCISE MY SOUL
Meditate, read the Bible, listen to spiritual music

How am I feeling today?

_____

_____

_____

_____

What triggers did I experience today?

_____

_____

_____

_____

HOW WAS MY ATTITUDE TODAY?

Score 1 to 5, 1 being the lowest, 5 being the highest.

| 1 | 2 | 3 | 4 | 5 |

HOW WAS MY ACTIVITY TODAY?

Score 1 to 5, 1 being the lowest, 5 being the highest.

| 1 | 2 | 3 | 4 | 5 |

Notes: _____

_____

_____

Set your intention for the day:

_____

_____

☐

Repeat my daily affirmation

· DAILY GRATITUDE ·

I am grateful for:

1. _____

2. _____

3. _____

☐ **EXERCISE MY MIND**
Play brain games, learn something new, read ten pages from a book

☐ **EXERCISE MY BODY**
Go for a walk, lift weights, do yoga, ride a bike

☐ **EXERCISE MY SOUL**
Meditate, read the Bible, listen to spiritual music

72

How am I feeling today?

_____

_____

_____

_____

What triggers did I experience today?

_____

_____

_____

HOW WAS MY ATTITUDE TODAY?

Score 1 to 5, 1 being the lowest, 5 being the highest.

| 1 | 2 | 3 | 4 | 5 |

HOW WAS MY ACTIVITY TODAY?

Score 1 to 5, 1 being the lowest, 5 being the highest.

| 1 | 2 | 3 | 4 | 5 |

Notes: _____

_____

_____

Set your intention for the day:

_____

_____

☐

Repeat my daily affirmation

· DAILY GRATITUDE ·

I am grateful for:

1. _____

2. _____

3. _____

☐ **EXERCISE MY MIND**
Play brain games, learn something new, read ten pages from a book

☐ **EXERCISE MY BODY**
Go for a walk, lift weights, do yoga, ride a bike

☐ **EXERCISE MY SOUL**
Meditate, read the Bible, listen to spiritual music

How am I feeling today?

_____

_____

_____

_____

What triggers did I experience today?

_____

_____

_____

_____

HOW WAS MY ATTITUDE TODAY?

Score 1 to 5, 1 being the lowest, 5 being the highest.

| 1 | 2 | 3 | 4 | 5 |

HOW WAS MY ACTIVITY TODAY?

Score 1 to 5, 1 being the lowest, 5 being the highest.

| 1 | 2 | 3 | 4 | 5 |

Notes: _____

_____

_____

Set your intention for the day:

_____

_____

☐

Repeat my daily affirmation

· DAILY GRATITUDE ·

I am grateful for:

1. _____

2. _____

3. _____

☐ **EXERCISE MY MIND**
Play brain games, learn something new, read ten pages from a book

☐ **EXERCISE MY BODY**
Go for a walk, lift weights, do yoga, ride a bike

☐ **EXERCISE MY SOUL**
Meditate, read the Bible, listen to spiritual music

How am I feeling today?

_____

_____

_____

_____

What triggers did I experience today?

_____

_____

_____

HOW WAS MY ATTITUDE TODAY?

Score 1 to 5, 1 being the lowest, 5 being the highest.

| 1 | 2 | 3 | 4 | 5 |

HOW WAS MY ACTIVITY TODAY?

Score 1 to 5, 1 being the lowest, 5 being the highest.

| 1 | 2 | 3 | 4 | 5 |

Notes: _____

_____

_____

Set your intention for the day:

_____

_____

☐

Repeat my daily affirmation

· DAILY GRATITUDE ·

I am grateful for:

1. _____

2. _____

3. _____

☐ **EXERCISE MY MIND**
Play brain games, learn something new, read ten pages from a book

☐ **EXERCISE MY BODY**
Go for a walk, lift weights, do yoga, ride a bike

☐ **EXERCISE MY SOUL**
Meditate, read the Bible, listen to spiritual music

How am I feeling today?

_____

_____

_____

_____

What triggers did I experience today?

_____

_____

_____

HOW WAS MY ATTITUDE TODAY?

Score 1 to 5, 1 being the lowest, 5 being the highest.

| 1 | 2 | 3 | 4 | 5 |

HOW WAS MY ACTIVITY TODAY?

Score 1 to 5, 1 being the lowest, 5 being the highest.

| 1 | 2 | 3 | 4 | 5 |

Notes: _____

_____

_____

Set your intention for the day:

_____

_____

☐

Repeat my daily affirmation

· DAILY GRATITUDE ·

I am grateful for:

1. _____

2. _____

3. _____

☐ **EXERCISE MY MIND**
Play brain games, learn something new, read ten pages from a book

☐ **EXERCISE MY BODY**
Go for a walk, lift weights, do yoga, ride a bike

☐ **EXERCISE MY SOUL**
Meditate, read the Bible, listen to spiritual music

How am I feeling today?

_____

_____

_____

_____

What triggers did I experience today?

_____

_____

_____

HOW WAS MY ATTITUDE TODAY?

Score 1 to 5, 1 being the lowest, 5 being the highest.

| 1 | 2 | 3 | 4 | 5 |

HOW WAS MY ACTIVITY TODAY?

Score 1 to 5, 1 being the lowest, 5 being the highest.

| 1 | 2 | 3 | 4 | 5 |

Notes: _____

_____

_____

Set your intention for the day:

_____

_____

☐

Repeat my daily affirmation

· DAILY GRATITUDE ·

I am grateful for:

1. _____

2. _____

3. _____

☐ **EXERCISE MY MIND**
Play brain games, learn something new, read ten pages from a book

☐ **EXERCISE MY BODY**
Go for a walk, lift weights, do yoga, ride a bike

☐ **EXERCISE MY SOUL**
Meditate, read the Bible, listen to spiritual music

How am I feeling today?

_____

_____

_____

_____

What triggers did I experience today?

_____

_____

_____

HOW WAS MY ATTITUDE TODAY?

Score 1 to 5, 1 being the lowest, 5 being the highest.

| 1 | 2 | 3 | 4 | 5 |

HOW WAS MY ACTIVITY TODAY?

Score 1 to 5, 1 being the lowest, 5 being the highest.

| 1 | 2 | 3 | 4 | 5 |

Notes: _____

_____

_____

Set your intention for the day:

_____

_____

☐

Repeat my daily affirmation

· DAILY GRATITUDE ·

I am grateful for:

1. _____

2. _____

3. _____

☐ **EXERCISE MY MIND**
Play brain games, learn something new, read ten pages from a book

☐ **EXERCISE MY BODY**
Go for a walk, lift weights, do yoga, ride a bike

☐ **EXERCISE MY SOUL**
Meditate, read the Bible, listen to spiritual music

How am I feeling today?

_____

_____

_____

_____

What triggers did I experience today?

_____

_____

_____

HOW WAS MY ATTITUDE TODAY?

Score 1 to 5, 1 being the lowest, 5 being the highest.

| 1 | 2 | 3 | 4 | 5 |

HOW WAS MY ACTIVITY TODAY?

Score 1 to 5, 1 being the lowest, 5 being the highest.

| 1 | 2 | 3 | 4 | 5 |

Notes: _____

_____

_____

Date:

Set your intention for the day:

_____

_____

☐

Repeat my daily affirmation

· DAILY GRATITUDE ·

I am grateful for:

1. _____

2. _____

3. _____

☐ ## EXERCISE MY MIND
Play brain games, learn something new, read ten pages from a book

☐ ## EXERCISE MY BODY
Go for a walk, lift weights, do yoga, ride a bike

☐ ## EXERCISE MY SOUL
Meditate, read the Bible, listen to spiritual music

How am I feeling today?

_____

_____

_____

_____

What triggers did I experience today?

_____

_____

_____

HOW WAS MY ATTITUDE TODAY?

Score 1 to 5, 1 being the lowest, 5 being the highest.

| 1 | 2 | 3 | 4 | 5 |

HOW WAS MY ACTIVITY TODAY?

Score 1 to 5, 1 being the lowest, 5 being the highest.

| 1 | 2 | 3 | 4 | 5 |

Notes: _____

_____

_____

Set your intention for the day:

_____

_____

☐

Repeat my daily affirmation

· DAILY GRATITUDE ·

I am grateful for:

1. _____

2. _____

3. _____

☐ **EXERCISE MY MIND**
Play brain games, learn something new, read ten pages from a book

☐ **EXERCISE MY BODY**
Go for a walk, lift weights, do yoga, ride a bike

☐ **EXERCISE MY SOUL**
Meditate, read the Bible, listen to spiritual music

How am I feeling today?

_____

_____

_____

_____

What triggers did I experience today?

_____

_____

_____

HOW WAS MY ATTITUDE TODAY?

Score 1 to 5, 1 being the lowest, 5 being the highest.

| 1 | 2 | 3 | 4 | 5 |

HOW WAS MY ACTIVITY TODAY?

Score 1 to 5, 1 being the lowest, 5 being the highest.

| 1 | 2 | 3 | 4 | 5 |

Notes: _____

_____

_____

Date:

Set your intention for the day:

☐

Repeat my daily affirmation

· DAILY GRATITUDE ·

I am grateful for:

1.
2.
3.

☐ **EXERCISE MY MIND**
Play brain games, learn something new, read ten pages from a book

☐ **EXERCISE MY BODY**
Go for a walk, lift weights, do yoga, ride a bike

☐ **EXERCISE MY SOUL**
Meditate, read the Bible, listen to spiritual music

How am I feeling today?

_____
_____
_____
_____

What triggers did I experience today?

_____
_____
_____

HOW WAS MY ATTITUDE TODAY?

Score 1 to 5, 1 being the lowest, 5 being the highest.

| 1 | 2 | 3 | 4 | 5 |

HOW WAS MY ACTIVITY TODAY?

Score 1 to 5, 1 being the lowest, 5 being the highest.

| 1 | 2 | 3 | 4 | 5 |

Notes: _____

_____
_____

Set your intention for the day:

_____

_____

☐

Repeat my daily affirmation

· DAILY GRATITUDE ·

I am grateful for:

1. _____

2. _____

3. _____

☐ **EXERCISE MY MIND**
Play brain games, learn something new, read ten pages from a book

☐ **EXERCISE MY BODY**
Go for a walk, lift weights, do yoga, ride a bike

☐ **EXERCISE MY SOUL**
Meditate, read the Bible, listen to spiritual music

How am I feeling today?

_____

_____

_____

_____

What triggers did I experience today?

_____

_____

_____

HOW WAS MY ATTITUDE TODAY?

Score 1 to 5, 1 being the lowest, 5 being the highest.

| 1 | 2 | 3 | 4 | 5 |

HOW WAS MY ACTIVITY TODAY?

Score 1 to 5, 1 being the lowest, 5 being the highest.

| 1 | 2 | 3 | 4 | 5 |

Notes: _____

_____

_____

Set your intention for the day:

⬚

Repeat my daily affirmation

· DAILY GRATITUDE ·

I am grateful for:

1.
2.
3.

☐ **EXERCISE MY MIND**
Play brain games, learn something new, read ten pages from a book

☐ **EXERCISE MY BODY**
Go for a walk, lift weights, do yoga, ride a bike

☐ **EXERCISE MY SOUL**
Meditate, read the Bible, listen to spiritual music

How am I feeling today?

_____

_____

_____

_____

What triggers did I experience today?

_____

_____

_____

HOW WAS MY ATTITUDE TODAY?

Score 1 to 5, 1 being the lowest, 5 being the highest.

| 1 | 2 | 3 | 4 | 5 |

HOW WAS MY ACTIVITY TODAY?

Score 1 to 5, 1 being the lowest, 5 being the highest.

| 1 | 2 | 3 | 4 | 5 |

Notes: _____

_____

_____

Set your intention for the day:

_____

_____

☐

Repeat my daily affirmation

· DAILY GRATITUDE ·

I am grateful for:

1. _____

2. _____

3. _____

☐ **EXERCISE MY MIND**
  Play brain games, learn something new, read ten pages from a book

☐ **EXERCISE MY BODY**
  Go for a walk, lift weights, do yoga, ride a bike

☐ **EXERCISE MY SOUL**
  Meditate, read the Bible, listen to spiritual music

How am I feeling today?

_____

_____

_____

_____

What triggers did I experience today?

_____

_____

_____

HOW WAS MY ATTITUDE TODAY?

Score 1 to 5, 1 being the lowest, 5 being the highest.

| 1 | 2 | 3 | 4 | 5 |

HOW WAS MY ACTIVITY TODAY?

Score 1 to 5, 1 being the lowest, 5 being the highest.

| 1 | 2 | 3 | 4 | 5 |

Notes: _____

_____

_____

Set your intention for the day:

_____

_____

☐

Repeat my daily affirmation

· DAILY GRATITUDE ·

I am grateful for:

1. _____

2. _____

3. _____

☐ **EXERCISE MY MIND**
Play brain games, learn something new, read ten pages from a book

☐ **EXERCISE MY BODY**
Go for a walk, lift weights, do yoga, ride a bike

☐ **EXERCISE MY SOUL**
Meditate, read the Bible, listen to spiritual music

How am I feeling today?

_____

_____

_____

_____

What triggers did I experience today?

_____

_____

_____

HOW WAS MY ATTITUDE TODAY?

Score 1 to 5, 1 being the lowest, 5 being the highest.

| 1 | 2 | 3 | 4 | 5 |

HOW WAS MY ACTIVITY TODAY?

Score 1 to 5, 1 being the lowest, 5 being the highest.

| 1 | 2 | 3 | 4 | 5 |

Notes: _____

_____

_____

Set your intention for the day:

_____

_____

☐

Repeat my daily affirmation

· DAILY GRATITUDE ·

I am grateful for:

1. _____

2. _____

3. _____

☐ **EXERCISE MY MIND**
Play brain games, learn something new, read ten pages from a book

☐ **EXERCISE MY BODY**
Go for a walk, lift weights, do yoga, ride a bike

☐ **EXERCISE MY SOUL**
Meditate, read the Bible, listen to spiritual music

How am I feeling today?

_____

_____

_____

_____

What triggers did I experience today?

_____

_____

_____

HOW WAS MY ATTITUDE TODAY?

Score 1 to 5, 1 being the lowest, 5 being the highest.

| 1 | 2 | 3 | 4 | 5 |

HOW WAS MY ACTIVITY TODAY?

Score 1 to 5, 1 being the lowest, 5 being the highest.

| 1 | 2 | 3 | 4 | 5 |

Notes: _____

_____

_____

Set your intention for the day:

☐

Repeat my daily affirmation

· DAILY GRATITUDE ·

I am grateful for:

1. ....

2. ....

3. ....

☐ **EXERCISE MY MIND**
Play brain games, learn something new, read ten pages from a book

☐ **EXERCISE MY BODY**
Go for a walk, lift weights, do yoga, ride a bike

☐ **EXERCISE MY SOUL**
Meditate, read the Bible, listen to spiritual music

How am I feeling today?

_____

_____

_____

_____

What triggers did I experience today?

_____

_____

_____

HOW WAS MY ATTITUDE TODAY?

Score 1 to 5, 1 being the lowest, 5 being the highest.

| 1 | 2 | 3 | 4 | 5 |

HOW WAS MY ACTIVITY TODAY?

Score 1 to 5, 1 being the lowest, 5 being the highest.

| 1 | 2 | 3 | 4 | 5 |

Notes: _____

_____

_____

Set your intention for the day:

_____

_____

☐

Repeat my daily affirmation

· DAILY GRATITUDE ·

I am grateful for:

1. _____

2. _____

3. _____

☐ **EXERCISE MY MIND**
Play brain games, learn something new, read ten pages from a book

☐ **EXERCISE MY BODY**
Go for a walk, lift weights, do yoga, ride a bike

☐ **EXERCISE MY SOUL**
Meditate, read the Bible, listen to spiritual music

How am I feeling today?

_____

_____

_____

_____

What triggers did I experience today?

_____

_____

_____

HOW WAS MY ATTITUDE TODAY?

Score 1 to 5, 1 being the lowest, 5 being the highest.

| 1 | 2 | 3 | 4 | 5 |

HOW WAS MY ACTIVITY TODAY?

Score 1 to 5, 1 being the lowest, 5 being the highest.

| 1 | 2 | 3 | 4 | 5 |

Notes: _____

_____

_____

Set your intention for the day:

_____

_____

☐

Repeat my daily affirmation

· DAILY GRATITUDE ·

I am grateful for:

1. _____

2. _____

3. _____

☐ **EXERCISE MY MIND**
Play brain games, learn something new, read ten pages from a book

☐ **EXERCISE MY BODY**
Go for a walk, lift weights, do yoga, ride a bike

☐ **EXERCISE MY SOUL**
Meditate, read the Bible, listen to spiritual music

How am I feeling today?

_____

_____

_____

_____

What triggers did I experience today?

_____

_____

_____

HOW WAS MY ATTITUDE TODAY?

Score 1 to 5, 1 being the lowest, 5 being the highest.

| 1 | 2 | 3 | 4 | 5 |

HOW WAS MY ACTIVITY TODAY?

Score 1 to 5, 1 being the lowest, 5 being the highest.

| 1 | 2 | 3 | 4 | 5 |

Notes: _____

_____

_____

Set your intention for the day:

_____

_____

☐

Repeat my daily affirmation

· DAILY GRATITUDE ·

I am grateful for:

1. _____

2. _____

3. _____

☐ **EXERCISE MY MIND**
Play brain games, learn something new, read ten pages from a book

☐ **EXERCISE MY BODY**
Go for a walk, lift weights, do yoga, ride a bike

☐ **EXERCISE MY SOUL**
Meditate, read the Bible, listen to spiritual music

How am I feeling today?

_____

_____

_____

_____

What triggers did I experience today?

_____

_____

_____

HOW WAS MY ATTITUDE TODAY?

Score 1 to 5, 1 being the lowest, 5 being the highest.

| 1 | 2 | 3 | 4 | 5 |

HOW WAS MY ACTIVITY TODAY?

Score 1 to 5, 1 being the lowest, 5 being the highest.

| 1 | 2 | 3 | 4 | 5 |

Notes: _____

_____

_____

Set your intention for the day:

_____

_____

□

Repeat my daily affirmation

· DAILY GRATITUDE ·

I am grateful for:

1. _____

2. _____

3. _____

□ **EXERCISE MY MIND**
Play brain games, learn something new, read ten pages from a book

□ **EXERCISE MY BODY**
Go for a walk, lift weights, do yoga, ride a bike

□ **EXERCISE MY SOUL**
Meditate, read the Bible, listen to spiritual music

How am I feeling today?

_____

_____

_____

_____

What triggers did I experience today?

_____

_____

_____

HOW WAS MY ATTITUDE TODAY?

Score 1 to 5, 1 being the lowest, 5 being the highest.

1 2 3 4 5

HOW WAS MY ACTIVITY TODAY?

Score 1 to 5, 1 being the lowest, 5 being the highest.

1 2 3 4 5

Notes: _____

_____

_____

Set your intention for the day:

_____

_____

☐

Repeat my daily affirmation

· DAILY GRATITUDE ·

I am grateful for:

1. _____

2. _____

3. _____

☐ **EXERCISE MY MIND**
Play brain games, learn something new, read ten pages from a book

☐ **EXERCISE MY BODY**
Go for a walk, lift weights, do yoga, ride a bike

☐ **EXERCISE MY SOUL**
Meditate, read the Bible, listen to spiritual music

How am I feeling today?

_____

_____

_____

_____

What triggers did I experience today?

_____

_____

_____

HOW WAS MY ATTITUDE TODAY?

Score 1 to 5, 1 being the lowest, 5 being the highest.

| 1 | 2 | 3 | 4 | 5 |

HOW WAS MY ACTIVITY TODAY?

Score 1 to 5, 1 being the lowest, 5 being the highest.

| 1 | 2 | 3 | 4 | 5 |

Notes: _____

_____

_____

Set your intention for the day:

_____

_____

☐

Repeat my daily affirmation

· DAILY GRATITUDE ·

I am grateful for:

1. _____

2. _____

3. _____

☐ **EXERCISE MY MIND**
Play brain games, learn something new, read ten pages from a book

☐ **EXERCISE MY BODY**
Go for a walk, lift weights, do yoga, ride a bike

☐ **EXERCISE MY SOUL**
Meditate, read the Bible, listen to spiritual music

How am I feeling today?

_____

_____

_____

_____

What triggers did I experience today?

_____

_____

_____

HOW WAS MY ATTITUDE TODAY?

Score 1 to 5, 1 being the lowest, 5 being the highest.

| 1 | 2 | 3 | 4 | 5 |

HOW WAS MY ACTIVITY TODAY?

Score 1 to 5, 1 being the lowest, 5 being the highest.

| 1 | 2 | 3 | 4 | 5 |

Notes: _____

_____

_____

Set your intention for the day:

_____

_____

☐

Repeat my daily affirmation

· DAILY GRATITUDE ·

I am grateful for:

1. _____

2. _____

3. _____

☐ **EXERCISE MY MIND**
Play brain games, learn something new, read ten pages from a book

☐ **EXERCISE MY BODY**
Go for a walk, lift weights, do yoga, ride a bike

☐ **EXERCISE MY SOUL**
Meditate, read the Bible, listen to spiritual music

How am I feeling today?

_____

_____

_____

_____

What triggers did I experience today?

_____

_____

_____

HOW WAS MY ATTITUDE TODAY?

Score 1 to 5, 1 being the lowest, 5 being the highest.

| 1 | 2 | 3 | 4 | 5 |

HOW WAS MY ACTIVITY TODAY?

Score 1 to 5, 1 being the lowest, 5 being the highest.

| 1 | 2 | 3 | 4 | 5 |

Notes: _____

_____

_____

Set your intention for the day:

_____

_____

☐

Repeat my daily affirmation

· DAILY GRATITUDE ·

I am grateful for:

1. _____

2. _____

3. _____

☐ **EXERCISE MY MIND**
Play brain games, learn something new, read ten pages from a book

☐ **EXERCISE MY BODY**
Go for a walk, lift weights, do yoga, ride a bike

☐ **EXERCISE MY SOUL**
Meditate, read the Bible, listen to spiritual music

How am I feeling today?

_____

_____

_____

_____

What triggers did I experience today?

_____

_____

_____

HOW WAS MY ATTITUDE TODAY?

Score 1 to 5, 1 being the lowest, 5 being the highest.

| 1 | 2 | 3 | 4 | 5 |

HOW WAS MY ACTIVITY TODAY?

Score 1 to 5, 1 being the lowest, 5 being the highest.

| 1 | 2 | 3 | 4 | 5 |

Notes: _____

_____

_____

Set your intention for the day:

_____

_____

☐

Repeat my daily affirmation

· DAILY GRATITUDE ·

I am grateful for:

1. _____

2. _____

3. _____

☐ **EXERCISE MY MIND**
Play brain games, learn something new, read ten pages from a book

☐ **EXERCISE MY BODY**
Go for a walk, lift weights, do yoga, ride a bike

☐ **EXERCISE MY SOUL**
Meditate, read the Bible, listen to spiritual music

How am I feeling today?

_____

_____

_____

_____

What triggers did I experience today?

_____

_____

_____

HOW WAS MY ATTITUDE TODAY?

Score 1 to 5, 1 being the lowest, 5 being the highest.

| 1 | 2 | 3 | 4 | 5 |

HOW WAS MY ACTIVITY TODAY?

Score 1 to 5, 1 being the lowest, 5 being the highest.

| 1 | 2 | 3 | 4 | 5 |

Notes: _____

_____

_____

Set your intention for the day:

_____

_____

☐

Repeat my daily affirmation

· DAILY GRATITUDE ·

I am grateful for:

1. _____

2. _____

3. _____

☐ **EXERCISE MY MIND**
Play brain games, learn something new, read ten pages from a book

☐ **EXERCISE MY BODY**
Go for a walk, lift weights, do yoga, ride a bike

☐ **EXERCISE MY SOUL**
Meditate, read the Bible, listen to spiritual music

How am I feeling today?

_____

_____

_____

_____

What triggers did I experience today?

_____

_____

_____

HOW WAS MY ATTITUDE TODAY?

Score 1 to 5, 1 being the lowest, 5 being the highest.

| 1 | 2 | 3 | 4 | 5 |

HOW WAS MY ACTIVITY TODAY?

Score 1 to 5, 1 being the lowest, 5 being the highest.

| 1 | 2 | 3 | 4 | 5 |

Notes: _____

_____

_____

Set your intention for the day:

_____

_____

☐

Repeat my daily affirmation

· DAILY GRATITUDE ·

I am grateful for:

1. _____

2. _____

3. _____

☐ **EXERCISE MY MIND**
Play brain games, learn something new, read ten pages from a book

☐ **EXERCISE MY BODY**
Go for a walk, lift weights, do yoga, ride a bike

☐ **EXERCISE MY SOUL**
Meditate, read the Bible, listen to spiritual music

How am I feeling today?

_____

_____

_____

_____

What triggers did I experience today?

_____

_____

_____

HOW WAS MY ATTITUDE TODAY?

Score 1 to 5, 1 being the lowest, 5 being the highest.

| 1 | 2 | 3 | 4 | 5 |

HOW WAS MY ACTIVITY TODAY?

Score 1 to 5, 1 being the lowest, 5 being the highest.

| 1 | 2 | 3 | 4 | 5 |

Notes: _____

_____

_____

Set your intention for the day:

_____

_____

☐

Repeat my daily affirmation

· DAILY GRATITUDE ·

I am grateful for:

1. _____

2. _____

3. _____

EXERCISE MY MIND
☐ *Play brain games, learn something new, read ten pages from a book*

EXERCISE MY BODY
☐ *Go for a walk, lift weights, do yoga, ride a bike*

EXERCISE MY SOUL
☐ *Meditate, read the Bible, listen to spiritual music*

How am I feeling today?

_____

_____

_____

_____

What triggers did I experience today?

_____

_____

_____

HOW WAS MY ATTITUDE TODAY?

Score 1 to 5, 1 being the lowest, 5 being the highest.

| 1 | 2 | 3 | 4 | 5 |

HOW WAS MY ACTIVITY TODAY?

Score 1 to 5, 1 being the lowest, 5 being the highest.

| 1 | 2 | 3 | 4 | 5 |

Notes: _____

_____

_____

Set your intention for the day:

_____

_____

☐

Repeat my daily affirmation

· DAILY GRATITUDE ·

I am grateful for:

1. _____

2. _____

3. _____

☐ **EXERCISE MY MIND**
Play brain games, learn something new, read ten pages from a book

☐ **EXERCISE MY BODY**
Go for a walk, lift weights, do yoga, ride a bike

☐ **EXERCISE MY SOUL**
Meditate, read the Bible, listen to spiritual music

How am I feeling today?

_____

_____

_____

_____

What triggers did I experience today?

_____

_____

_____

HOW WAS MY ATTITUDE TODAY?

Score 1 to 5, 1 being the lowest, 5 being the highest.

| 1 | 2 | 3 | 4 | 5 |

HOW WAS MY ACTIVITY TODAY?

Score 1 to 5, 1 being the lowest, 5 being the highest.

| 1 | 2 | 3 | 4 | 5 |

Notes: _____

_____

_____

Set your intention for the day:

_____

_____

☐

Repeat my daily affirmation

· DAILY GRATITUDE ·

I am grateful for:

1. _____

2. _____

3. _____

☐ **EXERCISE MY MIND**
Play brain games, learn something new, read ten pages from a book

☐ **EXERCISE MY BODY**
Go for a walk, lift weights, do yoga, ride a bike

☐ **EXERCISE MY SOUL**
Meditate, read the Bible, listen to spiritual music

How am I feeling today?

_____

_____

_____

_____

What triggers did I experience today?

_____

_____

_____

HOW WAS MY ATTITUDE TODAY?

Score 1 to 5, 1 being the lowest, 5 being the highest.

| 1 | 2 | 3 | 4 | 5 |

HOW WAS MY ACTIVITY TODAY?

Score 1 to 5, 1 being the lowest, 5 being the highest.

| 1 | 2 | 3 | 4 | 5 |

Notes: _____

_____

_____

Set your intention for the day:

☐

Repeat my daily affirmation

· DAILY GRATITUDE ·

I am grateful for:

1.
2.
3.

☐ **EXERCISE MY MIND**
Play brain games, learn something new, read ten pages from a book

☐ **EXERCISE MY BODY**
Go for a walk, lift weights, do yoga, ride a bike

☐ **EXERCISE MY SOUL**
Meditate, read the Bible, listen to spiritual music

How am I feeling today?

_____

_____

_____

_____

What triggers did I experience today?

_____

_____

_____

HOW WAS MY ATTITUDE TODAY?

Score 1 to 5, 1 being the lowest, 5 being the highest.

| 1 | 2 | 3 | 4 | 5 |

HOW WAS MY ACTIVITY TODAY?

Score 1 to 5, 1 being the lowest, 5 being the highest.

| 1 | 2 | 3 | 4 | 5 |

Notes: _____

_____

_____

Set your intention for the day:

_____

_____

☐

Repeat my daily affirmation

· DAILY GRATITUDE ·

I am grateful for:

1. ....

2. ....

3. ....

☐ **EXERCISE MY MIND**
Play brain games, learn something new, read ten pages from a book

☐ **EXERCISE MY BODY**
Go for a walk, lift weights, do yoga, ride a bike

☐ **EXERCISE MY SOUL**
Meditate, read the Bible, listen to spiritual music

How am I feeling today?

_____

_____

_____

_____

What triggers did I experience today?

_____

_____

_____

HOW WAS MY ATTITUDE TODAY?

Score 1 to 5, 1 being the lowest, 5 being the highest.

| 1 | 2 | 3 | 4 | 5 |

HOW WAS MY ACTIVITY TODAY?

Score 1 to 5, 1 being the lowest, 5 being the highest.

| 1 | 2 | 3 | 4 | 5 |

Notes: _____

_____

_____

Set your intention for the day:

_____

_____

☐

Repeat my daily affirmation

· DAILY GRATITUDE ·

I am grateful for:

1. _____

2. _____

3. _____

☐ **EXERCISE MY MIND**
Play brain games, learn something new, read ten pages from a book

☐ **EXERCISE MY BODY**
Go for a walk, lift weights, do yoga, ride a bike

☐ **EXERCISE MY SOUL**
Meditate, read the Bible, listen to spiritual music

How am I feeling today?

_____

_____

_____

_____

What triggers did I experience today?

_____

_____

_____

HOW WAS MY ATTITUDE TODAY?

Score 1 to 5, 1 being the lowest, 5 being the highest.

| 1 | 2 | 3 | 4 | 5 |

HOW WAS MY ACTIVITY TODAY?

Score 1 to 5, 1 being the lowest, 5 being the highest.

| 1 | 2 | 3 | 4 | 5 |

Notes: _____

_____

_____

Set your intention for the day:

....

....

☐

Repeat my daily affirmation

· DAILY GRATITUDE ·

I am grateful for:

1. ....

2. ....

3. ....

☐ **EXERCISE MY MIND**
Play brain games, learn something new, read ten pages from a book

☐ **EXERCISE MY BODY**
Go for a walk, lift weights, do yoga, ride a bike

☐ **EXERCISE MY SOUL**
Meditate, read the Bible, listen to spiritual music

How am I feeling today?

_____

_____

_____

_____

What triggers did I experience today?

_____

_____

_____

HOW WAS MY ATTITUDE TODAY?

Score 1 to 5, 1 being the lowest, 5 being the highest.

| 1 | 2 | 3 | 4 | 5 |

HOW WAS MY ACTIVITY TODAY?

Score 1 to 5, 1 being the lowest, 5 being the highest.

| 1 | 2 | 3 | 4 | 5 |

Notes: _____

_____

_____

Set your intention for the day:

_____

_____

☐

Repeat my daily affirmation

· DAILY GRATITUDE ·

I am grateful for:

1. _____

2. _____

3. _____

☐ **EXERCISE MY MIND**
Play brain games, learn something new, read ten pages from a book

☐ **EXERCISE MY BODY**
Go for a walk, lift weights, do yoga, ride a bike

☐ **EXERCISE MY SOUL**
Meditate, read the Bible, listen to spiritual music

How am I feeling today?

_____

_____

_____

_____

What triggers did I experience today?

_____

_____

_____

HOW WAS MY ATTITUDE TODAY?

Score 1 to 5, 1 being the lowest, 5 being the highest.

| 1 | 2 | 3 | 4 | 5 |

HOW WAS MY ACTIVITY TODAY?

Score 1 to 5, 1 being the lowest, 5 being the highest.

| 1 | 2 | 3 | 4 | 5 |

Notes: _____

_____

_____

Set your intention for the day:

_____

_____

☐

Repeat my daily affirmation

· DAILY GRATITUDE ·

I am grateful for:

1. ....

2. ....

3. ....

☐ **EXERCISE MY MIND**
Play brain games, learn something new, read ten pages from a book

☐ **EXERCISE MY BODY**
Go for a walk, lift weights, do yoga, ride a bike

☐ **EXERCISE MY SOUL**
Meditate, read the Bible, listen to spiritual music

How am I feeling today?

_____

_____

_____

_____

What triggers did I experience today?

_____

_____

_____

HOW WAS MY ATTITUDE TODAY?

Score 1 to 5, 1 being the lowest, 5 being the highest.

| 1 | 2 | 3 | 4 | 5 |

HOW WAS MY ACTIVITY TODAY?

Score 1 to 5, 1 being the lowest, 5 being the highest.

| 1 | 2 | 3 | 4 | 5 |

Notes: _____

_____

_____

Set your intention for the day:

_____

_____

☐

Repeat my daily affirmation

· DAILY GRATITUDE ·

I am grateful for:

1. _____

2. _____

3. _____

☐ **EXERCISE MY MIND**
Play brain games, learn something new, read ten pages from a book

☐ **EXERCISE MY BODY**
Go for a walk, lift weights, do yoga, ride a bike

☐ **EXERCISE MY SOUL**
Meditate, read the Bible, listen to spiritual music

How am I feeling today?

_____

_____

_____

What triggers did I experience today?

_____

_____

_____

HOW WAS MY ATTITUDE TODAY?

Score 1 to 5, 1 being the lowest, 5 being the highest.

| 1 | 2 | 3 | 4 | 5 |

HOW WAS MY ACTIVITY TODAY?

Score 1 to 5, 1 being the lowest, 5 being the highest.

| 1 | 2 | 3 | 4 | 5 |

Notes: _____

_____

_____

Set your intention for the day:

_____

_____

☐

Repeat my daily affirmation

· DAILY GRATITUDE ·

I am grateful for:

1. _____

2. _____

3. _____

☐ **EXERCISE MY MIND**
Play brain games, learn something new, read ten pages from a book

☐ **EXERCISE MY BODY**
Go for a walk, lift weights, do yoga, ride a bike

☐ **EXERCISE MY SOUL**
Meditate, read the Bible, listen to spiritual music

How am I feeling today?

_____

_____

_____

_____

What triggers did I experience today?

_____

_____

_____

HOW WAS MY ATTITUDE TODAY?

Score 1 to 5, 1 being the lowest, 5 being the highest.

| 1 | 2 | 3 | 4 | 5 |

HOW WAS MY ACTIVITY TODAY?

Score 1 to 5, 1 being the lowest, 5 being the highest.

| 1 | 2 | 3 | 4 | 5 |

Notes: _____

_____

_____

Set your intention for the day:

_____

_____

☐

Repeat my daily affirmation

· DAILY GRATITUDE ·

I am grateful for:

1. _____

2. _____

3. _____

☐ **EXERCISE MY MIND**
Play brain games, learn something new, read ten pages from a book

☐ **EXERCISE MY BODY**
Go for a walk, lift weights, do yoga, ride a bike

☐ **EXERCISE MY SOUL**
Meditate, read the Bible, listen to spiritual music

How am I feeling today?

_____

_____

_____

_____

What triggers did I experience today?

_____

_____

_____

HOW WAS MY ATTITUDE TODAY?

Score 1 to 5, 1 being the lowest, 5 being the highest.

| 1 | 2 | 3 | 4 | 5 |

HOW WAS MY ACTIVITY TODAY?

Score 1 to 5, 1 being the lowest, 5 being the highest.

| 1 | 2 | 3 | 4 | 5 |

Notes: _____

_____

_____

Date:

Set your intention for the day:

_____

_____

☐

Repeat my daily affirmation

· DAILY GRATITUDE ·

I am grateful for:

1. _____

2. _____

3. _____

☐ ## EXERCISE MY MIND
Play brain games, learn something new, read ten pages from a book

☐ ## EXERCISE MY BODY
Go for a walk, lift weights, do yoga, ride a bike

☐ ## EXERCISE MY SOUL
Meditate, read the Bible, listen to spiritual music

How am I feeling today?

_____

_____

_____

_____

What triggers did I experience today?

_____

_____

_____

_____

HOW WAS MY ATTITUDE TODAY?

Score 1 to 5, 1 being the lowest, 5 being the highest.

| 1 | 2 | 3 | 4 | 5 |

HOW WAS MY ACTIVITY TODAY?

Score 1 to 5, 1 being the lowest, 5 being the highest.

| 1 | 2 | 3 | 4 | 5 |

Notes: _____

_____

_____

Set your intention for the day:

....

....

☐

Repeat my daily affirmation

· DAILY GRATITUDE ·

I am grateful for:

1. ....

2. ....

3. ....

☐ **EXERCISE MY MIND**
Play brain games, learn something new, read ten pages from a book

☐ **EXERCISE MY BODY**
Go for a walk, lift weights, do yoga, ride a bike

☐ **EXERCISE MY SOUL**
Meditate, read the Bible, listen to spiritual music

How am I feeling today?

_____

_____

_____

_____

What triggers did I experience today?

_____

_____

_____

HOW WAS MY ATTITUDE TODAY?

Score 1 to 5, 1 being the lowest, 5 being the highest.

| 1 | 2 | 3 | 4 | 5 |

HOW WAS MY ACTIVITY TODAY?

Score 1 to 5, 1 being the lowest, 5 being the highest.

| 1 | 2 | 3 | 4 | 5 |

Notes: _____

_____

_____

Set your intention for the day:

_____

_____

☐

Repeat my daily affirmation

· DAILY GRATITUDE ·

I am grateful for:

1. ....

2. ....

3. ....

☐ **EXERCISE MY MIND**
Play brain games, learn something new, read ten pages from a book

☐ **EXERCISE MY BODY**
Go for a walk, lift weights, do yoga, ride a bike

☐ **EXERCISE MY SOUL**
Meditate, read the Bible, listen to spiritual music

How am I feeling today?

_____

_____

_____

_____

What triggers did I experience today?

_____

_____

_____

HOW WAS MY ATTITUDE TODAY?

Score 1 to 5, 1 being the lowest, 5 being the highest.

| 1 | 2 | 3 | 4 | 5 |

HOW WAS MY ACTIVITY TODAY?

Score 1 to 5, 1 being the lowest, 5 being the highest.

| 1 | 2 | 3 | 4 | 5 |

Notes: _____

_____

_____

Set your intention for the day:

_____

_____

☐

Repeat my daily affirmation

· DAILY GRATITUDE ·

I am grateful for:

1. ....

2. ....

3. ....

☐ **EXERCISE MY MIND**
Play brain games, learn something new, read ten pages from a book

☐ **EXERCISE MY BODY**
Go for a walk, lift weights, do yoga, ride a bike

☐ **EXERCISE MY SOUL**
Meditate, read the Bible, listen to spiritual music

156

How am I feeling today?

_____

_____

_____

_____

What triggers did I experience today?

_____

_____

_____

HOW WAS MY ATTITUDE TODAY?

Score 1 to 5, 1 being the lowest, 5 being the highest.

| 1 | 2 | 3 | 4 | 5 |

HOW WAS MY ACTIVITY TODAY?

Score 1 to 5, 1 being the lowest, 5 being the highest.

| 1 | 2 | 3 | 4 | 5 |

Notes: _____

_____

_____

Set your intention for the day:

_____

_____

☐

Repeat my daily affirmation

· DAILY GRATITUDE ·

I am grateful for:

1. ....

2. ....

3. ....

☐ **EXERCISE MY MIND**
Play brain games, learn something new, read ten pages from a book

☐ **EXERCISE MY BODY**
Go for a walk, lift weights, do yoga, ride a bike

☐ **EXERCISE MY SOUL**
Meditate, read the Bible, listen to spiritual music

How am I feeling today?

_____

_____

_____

_____

What triggers did I experience today?

_____

_____

_____

HOW WAS MY ATTITUDE TODAY?

Score 1 to 5, 1 being the lowest, 5 being the highest.

| 1 | 2 | 3 | 4 | 5 |

HOW WAS MY ACTIVITY TODAY?

Score 1 to 5, 1 being the lowest, 5 being the highest.

| 1 | 2 | 3 | 4 | 5 |

Notes: _____

_____

_____

Set your intention for the day:

_____

_____

☐

Repeat my daily affirmation

· DAILY GRATITUDE ·

I am grateful for:

1. ....

2. ....

3. ....

☐ ### EXERCISE MY MIND
Play brain games, learn something new, read ten pages from a book

☐ ### EXERCISE MY BODY
Go for a walk, lift weights, do yoga, ride a bike

☐ ### EXERCISE MY SOUL
Meditate, read the Bible, listen to spiritual music

How am I feeling today?

_____

_____

_____

_____

What triggers did I experience today?

_____

_____

_____

HOW WAS MY ATTITUDE TODAY?

Score 1 to 5, 1 being the lowest, 5 being the highest.

| 1 | 2 | 3 | 4 | 5 |

HOW WAS MY ACTIVITY TODAY?

Score 1 to 5, 1 being the lowest, 5 being the highest.

| 1 | 2 | 3 | 4 | 5 |

Notes: _____

_____

_____

Set your intention for the day:

_____

_____

☐

Repeat my daily affirmation

· DAILY GRATITUDE ·

I am grateful for:

1. _____

2. _____

3. _____

☐ **EXERCISE MY MIND**
Play brain games, learn something new, read ten pages from a book

☐ **EXERCISE MY BODY**
Go for a walk, lift weights, do yoga, ride a bike

☐ **EXERCISE MY SOUL**
Meditate, read the Bible, listen to spiritual music

How am I feeling today?

_____
_____
_____
_____

What triggers did I experience today?

_____
_____
_____

HOW WAS MY ATTITUDE TODAY?

Score 1 to 5, 1 being the lowest, 5 being the highest.

| 1 | 2 | 3 | 4 | 5 |

HOW WAS MY ACTIVITY TODAY?

Score 1 to 5, 1 being the lowest, 5 being the highest.

| 1 | 2 | 3 | 4 | 5 |

Notes: _____
_____
_____

Set your intention for the day:

_____

_____

[ ]

Repeat my daily affirmation

· DAILY GRATITUDE ·

I am grateful for:

1. _____

2. _____

3. _____

[ ] **EXERCISE MY MIND**
Play brain games, learn something new, read ten pages from a book

[ ] **EXERCISE MY BODY**
Go for a walk, lift weights, do yoga, ride a bike

[ ] **EXERCISE MY SOUL**
Meditate, read the Bible, listen to spiritual music

How am I feeling today?

_____

_____

_____

_____

What triggers did I experience today?

_____

_____

_____

HOW WAS MY ATTITUDE TODAY?

Score 1 to 5, 1 being the lowest, 5 being the highest.

| 1 | 2 | 3 | 4 | 5 |

HOW WAS MY ACTIVITY TODAY?

Score 1 to 5, 1 being the lowest, 5 being the highest.

| 1 | 2 | 3 | 4 | 5 |

Notes: _____

_____

_____

Set your intention for the day:

_____

_____

☐

Repeat my daily affirmation

· DAILY GRATITUDE ·

I am grateful for:

1. ....

2. ....

3. ....

☐ **EXERCISE MY MIND**
Play brain games, learn something new, read ten pages from a book

☐ **EXERCISE MY BODY**
Go for a walk, lift weights, do yoga, ride a bike

☐ **EXERCISE MY SOUL**
Meditate, read the Bible, listen to spiritual music

How am I feeling today?

_____

_____

_____

_____

What triggers did I experience today?

_____

_____

_____

HOW WAS MY ATTITUDE TODAY?

Score 1 to 5, 1 being the lowest, 5 being the highest.

| 1 | 2 | 3 | 4 | 5 |

HOW WAS MY ACTIVITY TODAY?

Score 1 to 5, 1 being the lowest, 5 being the highest.

| 1 | 2 | 3 | 4 | 5 |

Notes: _____

_____

_____

Set your intention for the day:

_____

_____

☐

Repeat my daily affirmation

· DAILY GRATITUDE ·

I am grateful for:

1. _____

2. _____

3. _____

☐ **EXERCISE MY MIND**
Play brain games, learn something new, read ten pages from a book

☐ **EXERCISE MY BODY**
Go for a walk, lift weights, do yoga, ride a bike

☐ **EXERCISE MY SOUL**
Meditate, read the Bible, listen to spiritual music

How am I feeling today?

_____

_____

_____

_____

What triggers did I experience today?

_____

_____

_____

HOW WAS MY ATTITUDE TODAY?

Score 1 to 5, 1 being the lowest, 5 being the highest.

| 1 | 2 | 3 | 4 | 5 |

HOW WAS MY ACTIVITY TODAY?

Score 1 to 5, 1 being the lowest, 5 being the highest.

| 1 | 2 | 3 | 4 | 5 |

Notes: _____

_____

_____

Set your intention for the day:

_____

_____

☐

Repeat my daily affirmation

· DAILY GRATITUDE ·

I am grateful for:

1. ....

2. _____

3. ....

☐ **EXERCISE MY MIND**
Play brain games, learn something new, read ten pages from a book

☐ **EXERCISE MY BODY**
Go for a walk, lift weights, do yoga, ride a bike

☐ **EXERCISE MY SOUL**
Meditate, read the Bible, listen to spiritual music

How am I feeling today?

_____

_____

_____

_____

What triggers did I experience today?

_____

_____

_____

HOW WAS MY ATTITUDE TODAY?

Score 1 to 5, 1 being the lowest, 5 being the highest.

| 1 | 2 | 3 | 4 | 5 |

HOW WAS MY ACTIVITY TODAY?

Score 1 to 5, 1 being the lowest, 5 being the highest.

| 1 | 2 | 3 | 4 | 5 |

Notes: _____

_____

_____

Set your intention for the day:

☐

Repeat my daily affirmation

· DAILY GRATITUDE ·

I am grateful for:

1.
2.
3.

☐ **EXERCISE MY MIND**
Play brain games, learn something new, read ten pages from a book

☐ **EXERCISE MY BODY**
Go for a walk, lift weights, do yoga, ride a bike

☐ **EXERCISE MY SOUL**
Meditate, read the Bible, listen to spiritual music

How am I feeling today?

_____

_____

_____

_____

What triggers did I experience today?

_____

_____

_____

HOW WAS MY ATTITUDE TODAY?

Score 1 to 5, 1 being the lowest, 5 being the highest.

| 1 | 2 | 3 | 4 | 5 |

HOW WAS MY ACTIVITY TODAY?

Score 1 to 5, 1 being the lowest, 5 being the highest.

| 1 | 2 | 3 | 4 | 5 |

Notes: _____

_____

_____

Set your intention for the day:

_____

_____

☐

Repeat my daily affirmation

· DAILY GRATITUDE ·

I am grateful for:

1. ....

2. ....

3. ....

☐ **EXERCISE MY MIND**
Play brain games, learn something new, read ten pages from a book

☐ **EXERCISE MY BODY**
Go for a walk, lift weights, do yoga, ride a bike

☐ **EXERCISE MY SOUL**
Meditate, read the Bible, listen to spiritual music

How am I feeling today?

_____

_____

_____

_____

What triggers did I experience today?

_____

_____

_____

HOW WAS MY ATTITUDE TODAY?

Score 1 to 5, 1 being the lowest, 5 being the highest.

| 1 | 2 | 3 | 4 | 5 |

HOW WAS MY ACTIVITY TODAY?

Score 1 to 5, 1 being the lowest, 5 being the highest.

| 1 | 2 | 3 | 4 | 5 |

Notes: _____

_____

_____

Set your intention for the day:

_____

_____

☐

Repeat my daily affirmation

· DAILY GRATITUDE ·

I am grateful for:

1. ....

2. ....

3. ....

☐ **EXERCISE MY MIND**
Play brain games, learn something new, read ten pages from a book

☐ **EXERCISE MY BODY**
Go for a walk, lift weights, do yoga, ride a bike

☐ **EXERCISE MY SOUL**
Meditate, read the Bible, listen to spiritual music

How am I feeling today?

_____

_____

_____

_____

What triggers did I experience today?

_____

_____

_____

HOW WAS MY ATTITUDE TODAY?

Score 1 to 5, 1 being the lowest, 5 being the highest.

| 1 | 2 | 3 | 4 | 5 |

HOW WAS MY ACTIVITY TODAY?

Score 1 to 5, 1 being the lowest, 5 being the highest.

| 1 | 2 | 3 | 4 | 5 |

Notes: _____

_____

_____

Set your intention for the day:

_____

_____

☐

Repeat my daily affirmation

· DAILY GRATITUDE ·

I am grateful for:

1. _____

2. _____

3. _____

☐ **EXERCISE MY MIND**
Play brain games, learn something new, read ten pages from a book

☐ **EXERCISE MY BODY**
Go for a walk, lift weights, do yoga, ride a bike

☐ **EXERCISE MY SOUL**
Meditate, read the Bible, listen to spiritual music

How am I feeling today?

_____

_____

_____

_____

What triggers did I experience today?

_____

_____

_____

HOW WAS MY ATTITUDE TODAY?

Score 1 to 5, 1 being the lowest, 5 being the highest.

| 1 | 2 | 3 | 4 | 5 |

HOW WAS MY ACTIVITY TODAY?

Score 1 to 5, 1 being the lowest, 5 being the highest.

| 1 | 2 | 3 | 4 | 5 |

Notes: _____

_____

_____

Set your intention for the day:

_____

_____

☐

Repeat my daily affirmation

· DAILY GRATITUDE ·

I am grateful for:

1. ....

2. ....

3. ....

☐ **EXERCISE MY MIND**
Play brain games, learn something new, read ten pages from a book

☐ **EXERCISE MY BODY**
Go for a walk, lift weights, do yoga, ride a bike

☐ **EXERCISE MY SOUL**
Meditate, read the Bible, listen to spiritual music

How am I feeling today?

_____

_____

_____

_____

What triggers did I experience today?

_____

_____

_____

HOW WAS MY ATTITUDE TODAY?

Score 1 to 5, 1 being the lowest, 5 being the highest.

| 1 | 2 | 3 | 4 | 5 |

HOW WAS MY ACTIVITY TODAY?

Score 1 to 5, 1 being the lowest, 5 being the highest.

| 1 | 2 | 3 | 4 | 5 |

Notes: _____

_____

_____

Set your intention for the day:

_____

_____

☐

Repeat my daily affirmation

· DAILY GRATITUDE ·

I am grateful for:

1. ....

2. ....

3. ....

☐ **EXERCISE MY MIND**
Play brain games, learn something new, read ten pages from a book

☐ **EXERCISE MY BODY**
Go for a walk, lift weights, do yoga, ride a bike

☐ **EXERCISE MY SOUL**
Meditate, read the Bible, listen to spiritual music

How am I feeling today?

_____

_____

_____

_____

What triggers did I experience today?

_____

_____

_____

HOW WAS MY ATTITUDE TODAY?

Score 1 to 5, 1 being the lowest, 5 being the highest.

| 1 | 2 | 3 | 4 | 5 |

HOW WAS MY ACTIVITY TODAY?

Score 1 to 5, 1 being the lowest, 5 being the highest.

| 1 | 2 | 3 | 4 | 5 |

Notes: _____

_____

_____

Set your intention for the day:

_____

_____

☐

Repeat my daily affirmation

· DAILY GRATITUDE ·

I am grateful for:

1. ....

2. ....

3. ....

☐ **EXERCISE MY MIND**
Play brain games, learn something new, read ten pages from a book

☐ **EXERCISE MY BODY**
Go for a walk, lift weights, do yoga, ride a bike

☐ **EXERCISE MY SOUL**
Meditate, read the Bible, listen to spiritual music

How am I feeling today?

_____

_____

_____

_____

What triggers did I experience today?

_____

_____

_____

_____

HOW WAS MY ATTITUDE TODAY?

Score 1 to 5, 1 being the lowest, 5 being the highest.

| 1 | 2 | 3 | 4 | 5 |

HOW WAS MY ACTIVITY TODAY?

Score 1 to 5, 1 being the lowest, 5 being the highest.

| 1 | 2 | 3 | 4 | 5 |

Notes: _____

_____

_____

185

Set your intention for the day:

....

....

☐

Repeat my daily affirmation

· DAILY GRATITUDE ·

I am grateful for:

1. ....

2. ....

3. ....

☐ **EXERCISE MY MIND**
Play brain games, learn something new, read ten pages from a book

☐ **EXERCISE MY BODY**
Go for a walk, lift weights, do yoga, ride a bike

☐ **EXERCISE MY SOUL**
Meditate, read the Bible, listen to spiritual music

How am I feeling today?

_____

_____

_____

_____

What triggers did I experience today?

_____

_____

_____

HOW WAS MY ATTITUDE TODAY?

Score 1 to 5, 1 being the lowest, 5 being the highest.

| 1 | 2 | 3 | 4 | 5 |

HOW WAS MY ACTIVITY TODAY?

Score 1 to 5, 1 being the lowest, 5 being the highest.

| 1 | 2 | 3 | 4 | 5 |

Notes: _____

_____

_____

Set your intention for the day:

_____

_____

☐

Repeat my daily affirmation

· DAILY GRATITUDE ·

I am grateful for:

1. _____

2. _____

3. _____

☐ **EXERCISE MY MIND**
Play brain games, learn something new, read ten pages from a book

☐ **EXERCISE MY BODY**
Go for a walk, lift weights, do yoga, ride a bike

☐ **EXERCISE MY SOUL**
Meditate, read the Bible, listen to spiritual music

How am I feeling today?

_____

_____

_____

_____

What triggers did I experience today?

_____

_____

_____

HOW WAS MY ATTITUDE TODAY?

Score 1 to 5, 1 being the lowest, 5 being the highest.

| 1 | 2 | 3 | 4 | 5 |

HOW WAS MY ACTIVITY TODAY?

Score 1 to 5, 1 being the lowest, 5 being the highest.

| 1 | 2 | 3 | 4 | 5 |

Notes: _____

_____

_____

Set your intention for the day:

_____

_____

☐

Repeat my daily affirmation

· DAILY GRATITUDE ·

I am grateful for:

1. ....

2. ....

3. ....

☐ **EXERCISE MY MIND**
Play brain games, learn something new, read ten pages from a book

☐ **EXERCISE MY BODY**
Go for a walk, lift weights, do yoga, ride a bike

☐ **EXERCISE MY SOUL**
Meditate, read the Bible, listen to spiritual music

How am I feeling today?

_____

_____

_____

_____

What triggers did I experience today?

_____

_____

_____

HOW WAS MY ATTITUDE TODAY?

Score 1 to 5, 1 being the lowest, 5 being the highest.

| 1 | 2 | 3 | 4 | 5 |

HOW WAS MY ACTIVITY TODAY?

Score 1 to 5, 1 being the lowest, 5 being the highest.

| 1 | 2 | 3 | 4 | 5 |

Notes: _____

_____

_____

Set your intention for the day:

_____

_____

☐

Repeat my daily affirmation

· DAILY GRATITUDE ·

I am grateful for:

1. _____

2. _____

3. _____

☐ **EXERCISE MY MIND**
Play brain games, learn something new, read ten pages from a book

☐ **EXERCISE MY BODY**
Go for a walk, lift weights, do yoga, ride a bike

☐ **EXERCISE MY SOUL**
Meditate, read the Bible, listen to spiritual music

How am I feeling today?

_____

_____

_____

_____

What triggers did I experience today?

_____

_____

_____

_____

HOW WAS MY ATTITUDE TODAY?

Score 1 to 5, 1 being the lowest, 5 being the highest.

| 1 | 2 | 3 | 4 | 5 |

HOW WAS MY ACTIVITY TODAY?

Score 1 to 5, 1 being the lowest, 5 being the highest.

| 1 | 2 | 3 | 4 | 5 |

Notes: _____

_____

_____

Set your intention for the day:

_____

_____

☐

Repeat my daily affirmation

· DAILY GRATITUDE ·

I am grateful for:

1. ....

2. ....

3. ....

☐ **EXERCISE MY MIND**
Play brain games, learn something new, read ten pages from a book

☐ **EXERCISE MY BODY**
Go for a walk, lift weights, do yoga, ride a bike

☐ **EXERCISE MY SOUL**
Meditate, read the Bible, listen to spiritual music

How am I feeling today?

_____

_____

_____

_____

What triggers did I experience today?

_____

_____

_____

HOW WAS MY ATTITUDE TODAY?

Score 1 to 5, 1 being the lowest, 5 being the highest.

| 1 | 2 | 3 | 4 | 5 |

HOW WAS MY ACTIVITY TODAY?

Score 1 to 5, 1 being the lowest, 5 being the highest.

| 1 | 2 | 3 | 4 | 5 |

Notes: _____

_____

_____

· *Final Thoughts* ·

We've reached the end, but my hope is that this daily task is now a daily habit that allows you to more easily set and reach your goals and accomplish your intention each and every day.

Don't stop here! Keep going! Make this a permanent part of your life and watch your life literally transform before your eyes.

The reason you write these things down is to look for patterns. Day after day, if you are being triggered by something, look for the pattern. That is the key to overcoming barriers. Some roadblocks are obvious, but more often than not, they are subtle and not easily detected.

What if you woke up every day knowing your intention for the day and also recognizing how to take all of the setbacks you encounter and use them to create opportunities? You can do this; this CAN be your reality.

You can't achieve any great thing by following the path of the majority. People choose that path when they don't have their own dreams, and they can't make their own way. The fear of failure will always be there. Let that fear remind you that you are on the right path.

If you want to build something great, it will require patience, time, courage, and consistency.

The person I am today is not the same person I was yesterday. And I plan to continue to grow and change tomorrow as well.

The same can be true for you, too. You were absolutely created to win. Let's go win!

· *Author Bio* ·

JM RYERSON is an author and entrepreneur who has been building companies and leading sales teams for more than 17 years. He is the chief leadership officer and managing vice president of Appreciation Financial. JM is also the author of the Amazon bestselling book, *Let's Go Win*, as well as the co-founder and CEO of Let's Go Win, a company dedicated to helping people around the world live their best lives. He has spent his career focused on enriching the lives of others while continuing to educate himself on best practices in leadership, vulnerability, and teamwork.

JM's great passion is helping his team members lead a life of fulfillment and become vulnerable and open to what life has in store for them. His ultimate goal is to give others the tools that will allow them to transcend their self-limiting beliefs. To JM, there is nothing more inspiring than to watch someone achieve more than they could ever imagine. That is why he considers it a real privilege to be even a small part of people's incredible journeys. JM lives in Boca Raton, Florida, with his wife, Lisa, and their two amazing boys.

Manufactured by Amazon.ca
Bolton, ON

29557429R00116